I wrote *Just Don't Give Up!* on a plane journey to Scotland to
attend the AIG Women's Open 2021 at Carnoustie Golf Links.

I'd accidentally left my headphones at home, so I had a
rare opportunity to just sit and think. I thought about all the
wonderful experiences the golf world had given me.

Golf is difficult. But if I'd given up, I wouldn't have had the
chance to enjoy the game in the same way I do now.
Nor would I have crossed paths with the incredible
people I've met along the way.

No matter your age, no matter your goal, sometimes
we all need a little reminder to *Just Don't Give Up!*

Mia xoxo

Just Don't Give Up!

WRITTEN BY

MIA BAKER

ILLUSTRATED BY

ALEXANDRA COLOMBO

This is Eddie.

This is Lola.

Eddie and Lola are best friends.

One day whilst Lola was on a walk, a small white ball rolled out in front of her. She picked it up, and put it in her pocket.

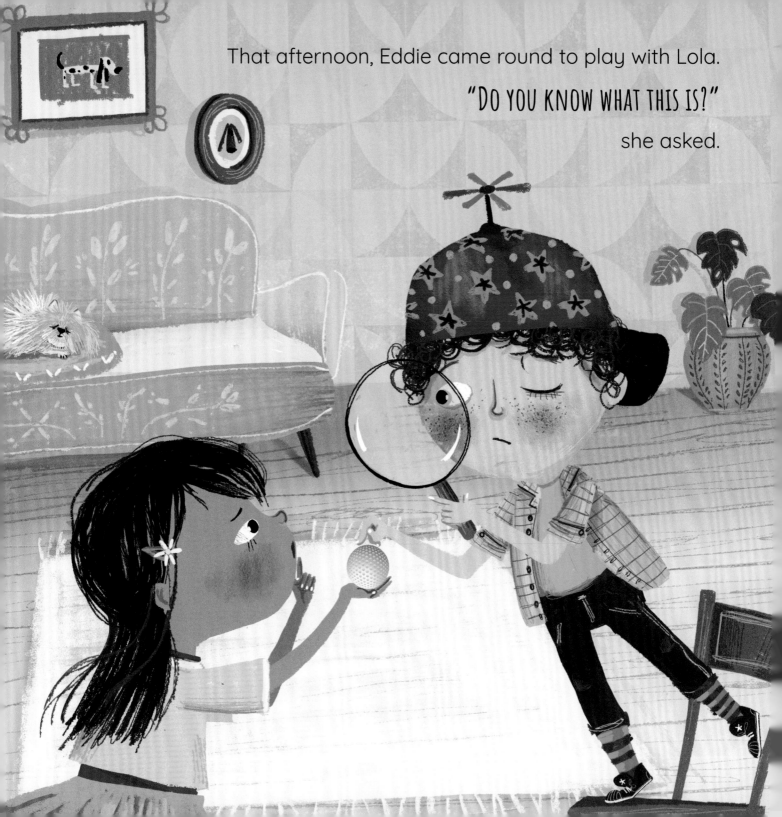

That afternoon, Eddie came round to play with Lola.

"DO YOU KNOW WHAT THIS IS?"

she asked.

"YES I DO! IT'S A GOLF BALL!"
said Eddie excitedly.

"A GOLF BALL?"
asked Lola, confused.

"YES! A GOLF BALL!"
cried Eddie.

Just then, Lola's mum walked in with some snacks.

"WHAT HAVE YOU GOT THERE?" she asked.

"A GOLF BALL",
replied Lola.

"OH THAT'S WONDERFUL!"
said Lola's mum.

"IN FACT, I HAVE SOME
GOLF CLUBS FROM WHEN I WAS
YOUR AGE IN THE GARAGE!"

They all headed into the garage to find Lola's mum's old golf clubs.

"HERE THEY ARE!"
said Lola's mum.

Lola's mum picked out a golf club
and gave it to Eddie and Lola.

"THIS IS MY OLD SAND WEDGE",

she said.

"WHAT'S A
SAND WEDGE?"

asked Eddie.

"A SAND WEDGE IS A GOLF CLUB
USED FOR SHORTER DISTANCES.
IT'S BUILT SO THAT THE BALL
CAN GO HIGH INTO THE AIR."

"IT'S A REALLY IMPORTANT
CLUB AND WILL MAKE YOU A
VERY GOOD GOLFER!"
explained Lola's mum.

Lola's mum
gave them
a bucket and
a bag of golf balls.

"TRY GETTING A GOLF BALL
INTO THE BUCKET",

she said.

"IT MIGHT BE HARD TO START WITH,
BUT IF YOU PRACTICE,
YOU'LL GET BETTER!"

Eddie and Lola spent all afternoon trying to hit golf balls into the bucket. At first they weren't very good and found it really really hard.

"I CAN'T DO IT!"
shouted Eddie.

"THIS IS TOO HARD!"
growled Lola.

"KEEP TRYING,"

said Lola's mum.

"THAT'S WHY WE HAVE LOTS OF BALLS
- SO YOU CAN PRACTICE!"

Eddie and Lola made a pact.
They were both going to get one golf
ball into the bucket before dinner.

Lola hit a ball and it knocked the bucket over.

"I NEARLY DID IT!" screamed Lola.

Then Eddie did the same.

"ME TOO!" shouted Eddie.

"KEEP GOING!" cheered Lola's mum.

"YOU CAN DO IT! AS LONG AS YOU...

...JUST DON'T GIVE UP!"

And just like that, Lola hit a ball and it popped right up into the air and landed straight into the bucket.

"WOO HOO!"

she shrieked.

"YOU CAN DO IT TOO Eddie!
JUST DON'T GIVE UP!"

Eddie kept
on trying...

and trying...

and trying...

But the ball kept on missing.

"I CAN'T DO IT!
IT'S TOO HARD!"
Eddie howled, and
started to cry.

"I BELIEVE IN YOU!"
said Lola.

"JUST DON'T GIVE UP!"

Eddie wiped away his tears and decided to keep on trying. Lola cheered as she watched Eddie hit the ball - each time getting closer and closer to the bucket.

"YOU'RE SO CLOSE!
YOU CAN DO IT!"
she said.

Just then, Eddie hit a beautiful, high shot that landed perfectly into the bucket!

"THAT WAS SO COOL!" shouted Eddie.

"IT'S DINNER TIME!" called Lola's mum.

"SHALL WE PLAY AGAIN TOMORROW?"
asked Eddie as they sat down for dinner.

"OKAY!" said Lola.
"DO YOU THINK WE CAN GET TWO BALLS
IN THE BUCKET TOMORROW?"

"DEFINITELY!" said Eddie. "AS LONG AS WE...

...JUST DON'T GIVE UP!"

"Golf is amazing for the mind. It helps you realise that you can overcome the things you thought you couldn't."

- Mia Baker